Little Shark Lulu is Sleeping

Dr Charlotte Birkmanis   Josie Montano   Carla Hoffenberg

IP Kidz
Brisbane

It is getting dark
in the ocean deep
and Little Shark Lulu
is nearly sound asleep ...

But some sea creatures are still out creeping
When Baby Clams emerge from their shells peeping
Lulu the Little Shark is no longer sleeping ...

Ssshhh

Octopus offspring like to hunt and dart
Catching their own lunch
because they're very smart ...

Ssshhh

Pint-sized Plankton are bobbing all about
As the ocean tides swish and churn them out ...

Ssshhh

Hat-sized Hatchet Fish are chasing Plankton
Their nightly adventure has only begun ...

Mini Mantis Shrimp cleans out his nest
to get dressed in his colourful clowning best ...

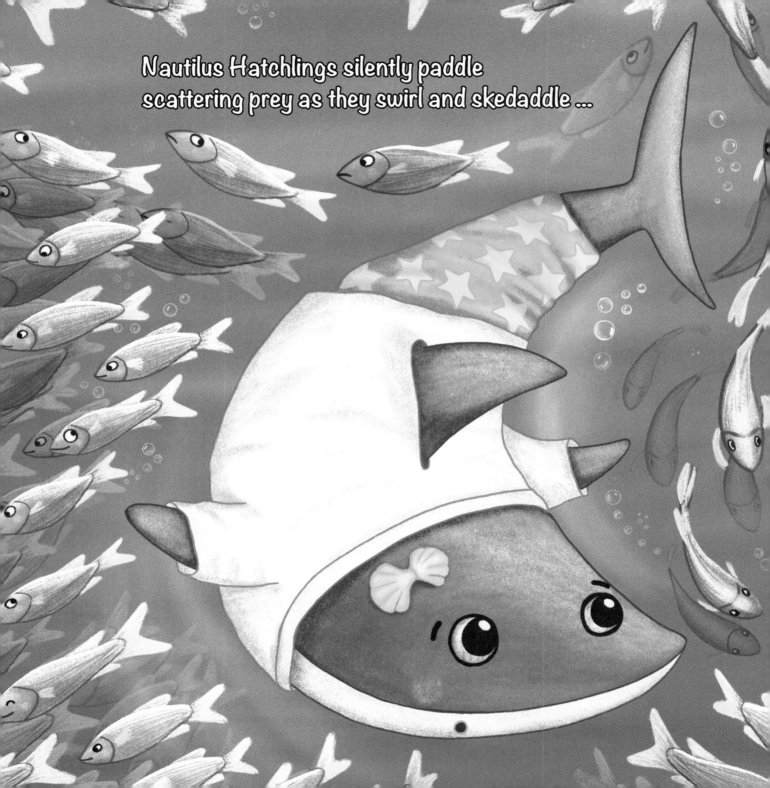

Nautilus Hatchlings silently paddle
scattering prey as they swirl and skedaddle ...

Ssshhh

A motionless suite of snoozing Sperm Whales
are sleeping heads up on their fluked tails ...

Small Squid is scared as she swims on her own. To be safe, she squirts ink into the unknown ...

Ssshhh

Petite Parrotfish nap in their cocoons
With beaks exposed, they will wake up soon ...

Ssshhh

Small Sea Snakes snort
at the ocean's surface

Coiled upside down
striking is their purpose ...

Ssshhh

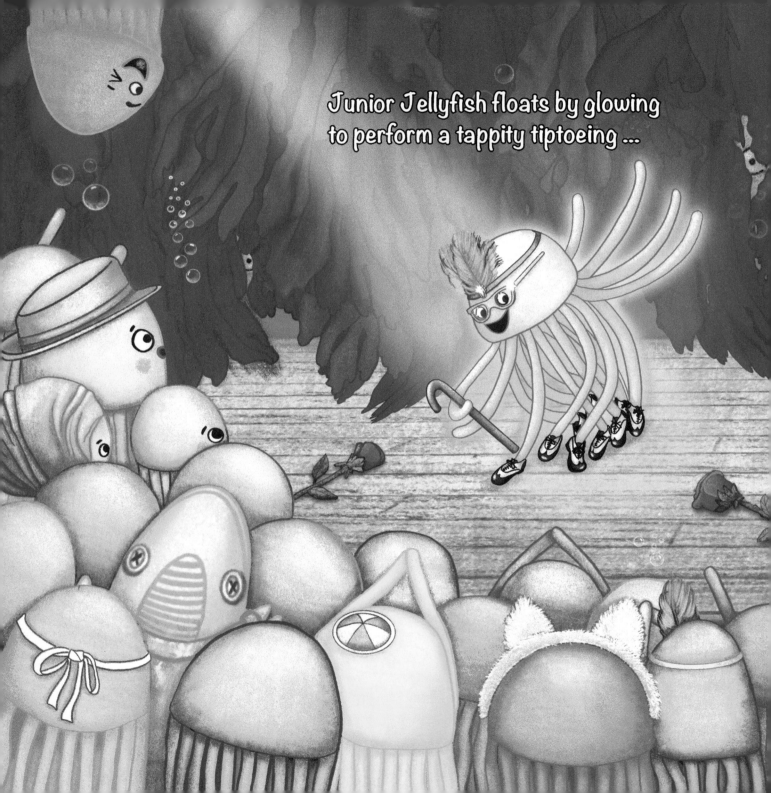

Junior Jellyfish floats by glowing
to perform a tappity tiptoeing ...

Sleepy Stingrays snuggle into the sand
camouflaged before they enter Dreamland ...

Ssshhh

A dainty dolphin pod
search for supper
When tired, they snooze
on the ocean's upper ...

Tiny Turtle Hatchlings
tuck into their shells
as they wait for deep
sleep to cast its spell ...

At last, it's quiet in the ocean deep
Good night, sleep tight, nobody make a peep ...

Little Ssshhh-ark Lulu is finally asleep ...

Ssshhh

IP Kidz
an imprint of Interactive Publications
Treetop Studio • 9 Kuhler Court
Carindale, Queensland, Australia 4152
sales@ipoz.biz
https://ipoz.biz

First published by IP Kidz, 2022
© Dr Charlotte Birkmanis, Josie Montano (text)
© Carla Hoffenberg (illustrations)
© David P Reiter (book design)

The moral rights of the creators have been asserted.

ISBN 9781922332929 (HB); ISBN 9781922332936 (eBk)

 A catalogue record for this book is available from the National Library of Australia

As a marine biologist, shark scientist and 'Public Relations Manager' for sharks and other predators, Charlotte spends lots of time at sea. Her research has taken her to 40+ countries to explore the secret lives of sharks. An award-winning science communicator, broadcast host, speaker and educator, Charlotte shares fun facts in English and Mandarin Chinese about co-existing with wildlife. An Australian STEM Ambassador, her work is widely published in scientific literature, but you might have seen it in your favourite show! Find out more at www.CharlotteBirkmanis.com

for my fin-tastic husband, James

Josie's an award-winning author with over 20 years experience and 60 resources internationally published within a variety of genres. She's also written and produced an award winning short film. As a storyteller she strives to advocate and give a voice to those who aren't able to, including Lulu the shark. Check her out at:
www.booksbyjosie.com.au

for my fin-tastic grandchildren, Venezia and Apollo — you are both jaw-some!

Carla is a children's book illustrator, residing in Sydney. She grew up in Johannesburg and lived in NYC. She is passionate about bringing joy to the world through optimistic and imaginative illustrations. Carla loves the beach, swimming, snorkelling and exploring local rock pools. Carla is always working on her next children's book project.
https://carlahoffenberg.com/

for Ty, Cody, Mason and Crackles

CPSIA information can be obtained
at www.ICGtesting.com
Printed in the USA
LVHW072354051022
730049LV00008B/191

9 781922 332929